Practise
Spelling
KS3
Age 11–14
Ron Simpson

● Contents

How to approach improving your spelling

Spelling can be confusing because the sound of a word is not always the same as its spelling. Despite what people say, there *are* rules in English spelling, but often there are as many exceptions as words which follow the rules. It is worthwhile learning the most important rules, but you also need to learn individual spellings. Most important of all is to take spelling seriously, but not to become anxious: it does not mean that you are poor at English if you have spelling problems.

How to use *Practise*

If you need to *practise*, this book explains the use of all the main spelling rules, looks at exceptions, lists some of the most common difficulties with spelling, then provides exercises to check your understanding. Before you start, you will need an exercise book of your own for copying and completing the exercises. As you work through the book, when you are confident that you have answered all the questions in an exercise correctly, move on to the next stage. If you feel you need more practice, follow a different explanation until you understand. On *Try it yourself!* pages you should do the activity *before* reading the notes at the side. When you are ready, photocopy the middle four pages of this book so that you can cut them up and do the activities. Make sure you keep the pieces in a safe place, such as an envelope, so that you do not lose them.

First published in 2007
exclusively for WHSmith by
Hodder Education, an Hachette UK company,
338 Euston Road
London NW1 3BH

Impression number   10 9 8 7 6 5 4
Year   2011
Text and illustrations © Hodder Murray 2007

Cover illustration by Sally Newton Illustrations

Typeset by Fakenham Photosetting Limited, Fakenham, Norfolk

Printed and bound in Spain

A CIP record for this book is available from the British Library

ISBN 978 0 340 94287 1

Sounds and spelling

Get started

The **vowels** are: *a, e, i, o, u,* and sometimes *y* (with a sound like *i*).

We could not speak (or have words) without vowels. They represent the basic open sounds people make when shouting, sighing or screaming. Most of the vowels can form words in their own right (*a, I, o/oh* and, if you are texting, *u*). Just imagine trying to say a word made up entirely of consonants: *rght* or *chldrn*, for example.

Practice

There are around 20 vowel sounds in English and only five vowels to make them, but, even so, the sound of a word can still be a guide to the spelling. Look at this chart of short and long vowel sounds:

Short	Long
can (baked beans, perhaps)	cane (no longer used in schools)
Ken (short for Kenneth)	keen (eager to do well)
fit (healthy, well-trained)	fight (a touch of violence)
cost (how much you pay)	coast (the shore)
cut (with scissors, perhaps)	cute (your favourite pop star)

By saying these words, you should be able to work out the sounds of long and short vowels.

Look at the **short** and **long vowels** in the chart above.

Did you notice four different ways in which vowels were made long?

- Add an *e* after the following consonant (as in *can/cane* or *cut/cute*).
- Double the *e* (as in *Ken/keen*).
- Add an extra, different vowel (as in *cost/coast*).
- Add silent consonants, usually *gh* (as in *fit/fight*).

The next section (**pages 5–6**) will go into more detail about the sounds and spellings of words that contain two vowels together.

Long and short vowels

A short vowel sound may be the letter name you first learned at infants' school, the sound that is made in:

cat, pen, sit, top, fun

The way these words are said may vary in different parts of the country, but the vowel is always short.

A long vowel sound is usually the 'name' of the vowel. Written down, they would look something like this:

ay, ee, eye, oh, yoo

Oo and *yoo*

A long *u* sound can be either *oo* or *yoo* (sounding like the name of the letter). Compare *rule* (pronounced 'rool') with *tune* (pronounced 'tyoon').

Of course, the *oo* sound can also be spelled 'oo' (*rule* rhymes with *fool*), but that is dealt with in the next section.

How to spell correctly

There is no magic way to spell correctly. In the end, you just have to learn some spellings that do not fit with any rules. But here are some steps towards good spelling:

- Learn the basic spelling rules. This will mean that you have a good chance of getting spellings right.
- You will be able to communicate clearly, but will make some mistakes.
- Many of the mistakes will be nearly right, near enough for you to use a dictionary. Keep a good dictionary handy and learn to use it correctly.
- Keep your own word book. Every time your teacher corrects a spelling or you need to look a word up in a dictionary, write it in your own word book.
- Your aim is:
  - to know the main spelling rules and any spellings you use that break the rules
  - to have both a dictionary and a word book to refer to
  - to feel that, when you hear a word, you have a good chance of spelling it correctly.

Try it yourself!

The long and short of it

Here are some short words for you to look at. In your exercise book, copy the table below them.

In each case, decide whether the vowel is **long** or **short**. Write it in the correct column of the table in your exercise book, then complete the rest of the line. The first two have been done for you.

light	ran	best	fine	coat	hit
reed	hop	bran	tun (an old word for 'barrel')		

Short	Long	What makes the vowel long?
lit	light	silent *gh* added
ran	rain	extra vowel added

Check your answers on **pages 31–32**.

All correct?

If you had any difficulties in the third column, do not worry, but, if you have made mistakes in the other two columns, go back to **page 3** and check the difference between long and short vowels.

Using a dictionary

Turn to the activity on **page 15**.

Remember the rules for using a dictionary:

- The words are arranged alphabetically.
- First look for the correct order using the first letter.
- If the first letter is the same, go on to the second letter.
- If the second is the same, go on to the third, the fourth and so on.

When you have finished, write out the words in your exercise book, in the order they would appear in a dictionary.

Check the answers on **pages 31–32** and correct any mistakes you have made.

More vowel sounds

Get started

Short vowel sounds can be changed into long sounds by:

- doubling the vowel
- adding another vowel
- adding silent consonants
- adding *e* after the following consonant.

Practice

Is it always this simple?

Unfortunately not. There are four complications:

- You may know that a word contains a long vowel and you must show this in the spelling, but how do you know the correct way? Only by learning the spelling of the word – or comparing the sound to other similar words.

- Sometimes words that sound the same have different spellings and different meanings. See the note **Which is which?** on the right.

- Sometimes two vowels are joined together to make a long sound that is different from the sound that either of the vowels makes singly. For example, *noise* has *o* and *i* together, but the sound that they make is 'oy'. This sound can be made by the letters *oy*, too. *Oy* is more likely to come at the end of a word, *oi* more likely in the middle.

- Occasionally a long vowel is formed by *two* of the methods mentioned. The word *height* is very unusual. It has a long *i* sound, but does it really need that extra *e* as well as the silent *gh*? After all, *light* and *fight* (not to mention *high*) do not need it. To help you remember: *height* and *weight* often go together.

If you find this confusing, the best thing to do is to learn the spellings of words you use frequently, practise them and build up your confidence.

Which is which?

Quite often, several words exist which sound the same, but have different meanings and spellings. How do you know which spelling to use?

Sometimes you do not, except by learning the right one.

Sometimes you can work it out from the spellings of other words.

Here are some common examples (by no means a full list) based on **long vowels**:

- A long *e* is often made by doubling the *e* or adding *a*. There are many words where both of these exist: *see* (use your eyes)/*sea* (expanse of water); *meet* (encounter)/*meat* (food); *week* (seven days)/*weak* (feeble); *deer* (animal)/*dear* (expensive or much loved).

- A long *a* is often made by adding *i* or an extra *e* after the consonant: *maid* (household servant)/*made* (built); *main* (chief)/*mane* (lion's hair); *pain* (hurt)/*pane* (glass).

- A long *i* can be made by a silent *gh* or a final *e*. Think of *right* (correct or opposite of left) and *write* (use your pen). Note the silent *w* in the second version; see **pages 9–10**.

- Sometimes words that look completely different sound the same. For instance, *bear* (the animal or to carry) sounds like *bare* (naked), but is spelled like *fear*, *near* or *rear.*

(See **pages 23–26** for more about Same sound, different spelling.)

Two more exceptions

Calling all cars!

Some consonants, following a long vowel, affect the sound of the vowel. Two of the most common are in Calling all cars! Double *l*, following an *a*, produces a sound rather like 'orl'. But avoid spelling it that way in words like *tall* and *fall*. (The same sound can be spelled *aw*, as in *bawl* and *trawl*.) If *a*, *o* or *u* is followed by *r*, a change in the vowel sound is produced (as in *car*, *or* or *blur*), but this is not usually a spelling problem.

Read this carefully

It makes sense that *red* (the colour) is spelled as it is. It makes sense that *read* (as in *I want to read my book*) is spelled as it is. But what about:

I've already read that book.

It should really be a long *e*, but it is not. And you will find the same happens in *bread* and *tread* (not to mention *already*).

A difficult word

The word for two vowel sounds merging into one is a *diphthong*. Sometimes you will see two vowels together which are sounded separately (*friar*, *usual*, *chaos*). These are *not* diphthongs.

Try it yourself!

Joining vowels together

This exercise deals with words that contain two vowels side by side making one sound.

- **The same vowel** – The only two vowels that normally double up are *e* and *o*. A double *e* just makes the vowel longer, but a double *o* makes a different sound. Compare the long *o* in *stone* with the double *o* in *spoon*.
- **Different vowels** – The most common are:
  - *ai*, *ea* and *oa* (and sometimes *ui*), which all make the first vowel long (exceptions include *said* which is pronounced 'sed')
  - *au*, *oi* and *ou*, which all make a different sound, all of them something like a shout or cry of pain: *Aw* or *Ah! Oy! Ow!* (exceptions include *you* – 'yoo' – and *youth* – 'yooth')
  - *ua*, which is unusual as the *u* sometimes makes a sort of *w* sound, but is most often silent
  - *ie* and *ei*, which are dealt with in *I before E* (pages 13–14).

In the following sentences, some pairs of vowels have been left out of words. Copy the sentences into your exercise book and try to insert the correct vowels. The sentences should make it obvious which words you need.

It's such a n____sance trying to find out whose f____lt it was.

The book's too d____r for me, but I hope to pers____de my ____nt to buy it.

Bec__se of his sore t____th, he had a r____lly p____ned expression on his face.

I left my best c____t on the tr____n.

'That's sp____led the party,' she w____led.

'I'm not t____ k____n on j____ning the others,' he s____d.

Check your answers on **pages 31–32**.

All correct?

If you have made any mistakes, check the right answer and write it in your word book.

Some notes on consonants

Get started

Consonants are the letters in the alphabet which are not vowels: *b, c, d, f, g, h, j, k, l, m, n, p, q, r, s, t, v, w, x, y* (usually), *z*.

Unlike vowels, consonants tend to make the same sound (or, at least, a very similar sound) most of the time. You should be able to tell the difference between *b* and *d*, or *m* and *n*, without too much trouble.

However, *g* and *c* both have two distinct sounds, a **hard** one and a **soft** one:

- A hard *c* is the same sound as a *k*. You will find it at the beginning of words like *catch*, *copper* and *customer*. A soft *c* is the same sound as an *s*. You will find it at the beginning of words like *cell* and *cinema*.
- The pattern is similar for *g*. A *gorge* in the mountains begins with a hard *g*, the name *George* begins with a soft *g*.

This can help with your spelling because there is a rule about the vowel that follows a *c* or *g*. Can you work it out from the examples given above?

The rule is:

- A soft *c* or *g* is followed by *e* or *i*.
- A hard *c* or *g* is followed by *a, o* or *u* – or by another consonant – or is the last letter.

There are exceptions (*gig* and *giggle* both begin with a hard *g*, for instance), but this is a fairly safe rule for your spelling.

Practice

Try this little exercise. Think of ten words beginning with *c*, five beginning with a sound like *k*, five beginning with a sound like *s*. Write them down, making sure that the *k* sound is followed by *a, o* or *u* and the *s* sound is followed by *e* or *i*. Then check your spellings in a dictionary.

You will often find two or more consonants together in a word. Often they just make their normal sounds one after the other, so spelling is straightforward. If you want to spell *stressing* correctly, just write it as it sounds: the *str* sounds can all be heard, as can the *ng* sounds. As for *ss*, the section on **pages 11–12** deals with **Double letters**.

Watch out for the way in which *h* changes the sound of another consonant: *th, sh, ch, tch*, etc. In particular, *ph* is sometimes the correct spelling for the *f* sound: *physics, phenomenal*, etc. Do not mix up words like *physical* (with *ph* for *f*) with words like *psychology* (with a silent *p*).

There is no such word as *phsychology*.

And remember that the 'sh' sound can sometimes be made by different combinations of letters: *sc, ss* or even *s* or *t* followed by *i* (*attention*).

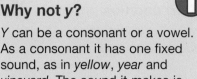

Why not *y*?

Y can be a consonant or a vowel. As a consonant it has one fixed sound, as in *yellow*, *year* and *vineyard*. The sound it makes is clearly a consonant. But *y* can also make an *i* sound, particularly in three situations:

- In the *-ly* word ending, it makes the sound of a short *i*: *lively, quickly, neatly, friendly*, etc. Note that this is always spelled *ly*; there is never an extra *e*. This is often thought of as an adverb ending, which it is, but it is also widely used for adjectives – see *Practise Grammar*.
- *Y* is also used in several difficult, but fairly common, words of Greek origin. Try not to confuse the words which come from *crystal* and *crypt* (which have no *h*), with words like *chrysanthemum* and *chrysalis* (which have an *h*). Then there are words like *physical* (short *i* sound) and *psyche* (long *i* sound). (See the text on the left.)
- *Y* can also be linked with another vowel in words like *way, key* and *toy*. This usually presents no spelling problem, except perhaps with plurals. (See page 19, How to form plurals.)

Two oddities

You may notice that number 5 in the activity on the right uses *y* as a vowel. Just like *i*, it makes the *g* soft.

Now look at number 10. Although the *g* is followed by *i*, it is still hard because *singing* comes from the word *sing*. There is also a word *singe*, meaning 'to burn'. Which of the following do you think is correct?

A hot coal fell out of the fire, singing the carpet.

A hot coal fell out of the fire, singeing the carpet.

Usually *e* drops out before an ending like *-ing* is added, but not this time. The second sentence is correct, reminding us that the *g* is soft. Note also the same thing happening in words like *noticeable* and *outrageous* (or *courageous* in number 9). In the same way, the *u* in *rogue* shows that the *g* is hard.

Try it yourself!

How hard is this?

Below are clues to twelve words. The answers are not very difficult to work out, but it is essential that they are spelled correctly. All of them contain at least one **hard** or **soft** *c* or *g*.

Remember the rule: hard before a consonant or *a, o* or *u*, soft before *e* or *i*. The first one is done for you. Write the answers to the remaining clues in your exercise book.

1 football or tennis perhaps (hard *g* at beginning) **game**
2 prisoner's room (soft *c* at beginning)
3 played at Lord's (hard *c* at beginning and in middle)
4 enormous (soft *g* at beginning, then hard *g*, hard *c* at end)
5 where you work out or do PE (soft *g* at beginning)
6 absolutely beautiful (hard *g* at beginning, soft *g* in middle)
7 cappuccino, maybe (hard *c* at beginning)
8 power (may it be with you!) (soft *c* near end)
9 very brave (hard *c* at beginning, soft *g* in middle)
10 performing a song (hard *g* in middle and at end)
11 the subject is the world (soft *g* at beginning, hard *g* in middle)
12 the middle, maybe a town (soft *c* at beginning)

Check the answers on **pages 31–32**.

All correct?

If you did not work out one or two of the answers, do not worry.

If you made a spelling mistake, go back to the rules on **page 7** and check your answer.

Fill the gaps

Copy the following words into your exercise book. The gaps in each of them can be filled by two or three letters (mostly consonants). Clues are given when necessary.

___otogra___y	ma___ ___es (lights)	con___ien___ous
___ychology	ma___ematics	___oe-___ine (same letters each time)
___eatre	ma___ed (like potatoes)	___ur___ (same letters each time)

Check your answers on **pages 31–32**.

All correct?

If not, do not worry: there are some very difficult words here. Just copy them into your word book and learn them.

Silent letters

Get started

What are now **silent letters** were not always silent. At first they were sounded, but over the years people have said the words in a way that seemed easier. Sometimes the letters have stayed when the sounds have disappeared.

Just think of a few English cities. We say *Gloster* and *Wooster* though they are still spelled *Gloucester* and *Worcester.*

But what about *Nottingham*? Officially we still say *Not-ting-ham*, but you have probably heard people say *Nott-num.* It is easy to see how the changes come about.

Some patterns of silent letters

b	often follows *m* at the end of a word	*climb, dumb*
	or comes before *t*	*debt, subtle*
ch/gh	*gh* can make a vowel long,	*light, fight*
	but both *ch* and *gh* can be silent in front of *t*	*thought, yacht*
	or *gh* can be silent at the end of a word	*though*
g	usually followed by *n* at the start of a word	*gnaw, gnome*
h	in some words it is silent at the beginning	*hour, honest*
	and it can be silent after *r* or *g*	*ghastly, rhinoceros*
k	like *g*, followed by *n* at the start of a word	*knight, kneel*
n	can be silent after *m*	*hymn, column*
p	at the start of a word, followed by *n* or *s*	*pneumonia, psychology*
s	sometimes silent before *l* in the middle of a word	*isle, aisle*
t	is not sounded in *-stl-* combinations	*whistle, thistle*
w	often silent before *r* at the start of a word	*wrong, wrap*

(See also **Complications** on **page 10**.)

Learning this list is not enough. You need to learn words individually as well.

Perhaps if you studied the histories of the words, you would find out why *know* is not spelled *gnow* and *gnaw* is not spelled *knaw*. But it is much easier just to learn the right spelling.

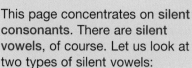

Silent vowels

This page concentrates on silent consonants. There are silent vowels, of course. Let us look at two types of silent vowels:

- **The silent *e*** – At the end of a word, *e* is almost always silent if it follows a consonant. But what does that do to the word? Very often, nothing, especially following *v*. Words like *have, live, active, possessive* and *demonstrative* would sound the same without *e*, but words ending in *v* look odd. In some cases, *e* makes a vowel long: *cane, cute*, etc. (See page 3.)

- **Inexact vowel sounds** – Many vowel sounds are not exact which makes spelling more difficult. People who say *I should of*, instead of *I should have*, probably write it as well. So it is difficult sometimes to identify the exact sound of a vowel. Is the *u* in *disguise* or *biscuit* a silent letter? Or the *u* in *behaviour* or *colour*? Or even the *i* in *seize*? The rules for consonants are much clearer.

Complications

Sometimes it is difficult to lay down rules. The letter *l*, for instance, can be silent, but it usually alters the sound of the vowel:

In *yolk* or *folk* it makes the vowel long.

In *palm* or *calm* it alters the *a* sound to something like 'ar'.

But what about the silent *w*?

- You have met the silent *w* at the start of a word before *r*: *wrinkle*, *wrestler*.
- What about *answer* or *sword*? These use a silent *w* following *s*.
- Or the *w* at the end of a word following *o* or *a*? *Know* actually begins and ends with a silent letter: two out of four!
- And how to explain the silent *w* in *two*? Do not explain, but remember it. *To*, *two* and *too* are dealt with in **Same sound, different spelling** on page 23.

Rules are very useful in giving you a start, but in the end you must *learn from examples*.

Try it yourself!

Fill in the silent letter

In the following words, a silent letter has been left out, occasionally more than one letter. Most of the letters – but not all! – are in the list on **page 9**. Copy the words into your exercise book and fill in the gaps.

__reck	__rinkle	thou___t
__nowledge	g__ost	s__issors
__nash	__nit	cas__le
r__ythm	ca__m	throu___out
de__t	ya___t	__nuckle
recei__t	mis__letoe	thum__
__rist	__neumatic	

Check the answers on **pages 31–32. All correct?**

If not, make sure that you know the rule, but, most important, write the spelling in your word book.

Spelling for meaning

Sometimes silent letters can make the difference between words that sound the same, but have different meanings. **Page 5** referred to *right/write*. There are in fact four words which are pronounced the same:

right	correct or opposite of left
write	what you do with letters or your homework
rite	a ceremony in a church or faith
wright	a maker, usually used now as a surname or with the thing made: *shipwright* or *playwright*

These four words are separated by silent letters and different ways of lengthening the vowel.

Copy the following sentences into your exercise book. Underline the correct spelling in each one.

Bobby Robson was made a night/knight for services to football.

The room was filled with an attractive sent/scent.

I new/knew all the rite/right/write/wright answers.

I no/know you have problems with your spelling.

You need to rap/wrap up warm.

My father told me to ring/wring the cloth dry.

Only a Boy Scout could have tied that not/knot.

Holy Communion is a rite/right/write/wright of the Church.

Check the answers on **pages 31–32. All correct?**

Now look at the **Complications** note on the left.

Double letters

Get started

In a word of two or more **syllables**, how do you decide whether the consonant in the middle should be **single** or **double**?

- What is the difference between *tiling* the bathroom and *tilling* the soil?
- Why is everything *shiny* on a *sunny* day?
- Why, when you were *hoping* for the best, were you *hopping* up and down with anxiety?

Have a closer look at the three examples above and try to work out the main rule for yourself.

Then read on to make sure you are right.

The rule for words of two syllables:

- If the first vowel is a *long* single vowel, it is followed by a *single* consonant: **Riding is what you do on your bike.**
- If the first vowel is a *short* single vowel, it is followed by a *double* consonant: **'Ridding' means getting rid of something.**

Practice

Here is a helpful hint, not really a rule, but something that works more often than not and helps you reach the right spelling. Look at what happens to one-syllable verbs when they have an extra syllable added:

- If the verb ends in *e* (long vowel – see **page 3**), for example *cane*, then remove *e* before adding the ending, to give *caning* (single consonant – long vowel).
- If the verb has a single vowel without *e* (short vowel), for example *can*, then double the consonant before adding the ending, to give *canning* (short vowel).

Remember: An *e* at the end and a single consonant in the middle are two ways of making a vowel long – and they often go together in different forms of the same word.

But be careful: this only applies when the added part begins with a vowel. So *hope* becomes *hoping*, but the *e* stays in *hopeless*.

A warning

Here is a warning, but watch out for exceptions.

Look at the word *double*. From its sound, we would expect it to be spelled *dubble*, a short *u* followed by a double consonant, just like *rubble* or *bubble*.

With its spelling, with the two vowels together (*ou*), we might expect a long vowel sound, 'ow', perhaps.

So once again remember that rules are only a guide. It is the only way to stay out of trouble (not *trubble*!).

Different consonants

It is probably better not to learn rules for two different consonants in the middle of a word. It all depends on the vowels and consonants.

So *nd* follows a long vowel in *finding* and *minding*, but a short one in *mending*.

Hedging and *ditching* are both short vowels, though *hedge* has lost an *e* and *ditch* has not.

If there is *just one consonant sound in the middle of a word*, make it single or double depending on whether the vowel before is long or short. You will *usually* be right.

Otherwise learn individual spellings and use common sense.

Problems with proper nouns

This is a good place to mention that proper nouns can pose problems in spellings. These are the individual names (with capital letters) that belong to people, places, organisations, brands, etc.

Places can be difficult and people can make their own choices of spelling, but most of the more frequent names for people stay within the rules:

- *Peter* has a long vowel followed by a single consonant; *Gemma* a short vowel followed by a double consonant.
- *Simon* has a long vowel, but, if you shorten the vowel, you add an extra consonant to create the surname *Simmons*.
- Names like *Amy* and *Jackie* follow the rules (*ck* counts as a double consonant), even if *Janet* does not.

However, you could have fun working out how many of your friends' names (or names of local towns, firms or streets) break the rules of spelling – maybe your own does!

Try it yourself!

According to the rule

Copy the following sentences into your exercise book. Each has one word or more with a consonant left out in the middle. The rest of the sentence should help you to work out which word or words are intended. Insert a **single** or **double** consonant. There are no exceptions to the rule given on **page 11**.

> Farmers fa__en turkeys for Christmas.
> As the light fa__ed, the children started ru__ing home for tea.
> When the winger cro__ed from the left, the full back tri__ed over his own feet.
> We went to co__ect the bread from the ba__er.
> You're not bla__ing me for that! It wasn't my fault.
> Over 30 pupils were cra__ed into a small classroom.
> The paint was fla__ing from the wall of the ba__ered building.
> She was cu__ing the material with a pair of sci__ors.
> At the top of the volcano we peered into the cra__er.
> You caught me na__ing.

Check your answers on **pages 31–32. All correct?**

If not, go back to **page 11** and re-read the rule.

Remember:

- A single consonant in the middle of the word usually means a long vowel before it.
- Use this rule on any words you do not know.
- Always be prepared for exceptions.

A mixed bag

Copy the following short piece of writing into your exercise book and underline the right spellings. There is a mixture of everything considered in this section – and some exceptions to the rule:

> Mr Grayson was hopful/hopeful of geting/getting out of prison/prisson. He knew he was innocent/inoccent. He had been on a baned/banned prottest/protest march, but had steerred/steered clear of any trubble/trouble. He had never/nevver commited/committed/comited any criminal/crimminal/criminnal act in his life before/beffore, so he was sure his arest/arrest was a mistake.

Check your answers on **pages 31–32. All correct?**

There are some easy answers, but also some tricky ones, so do not worry if you got one or two wrong. If you made a mistake on any words you are likely to use, it is time to take out your word book again.

I before E

Get started

This is the best-known and most helpful spelling rule in English, but only if you remember it in full:

I before *e* except after *c* when the sound is 'ee'

Practice

All these words make the same vowel sound ('ee') and use the letters *i* and *e*:

Not after c	After c
believe	perceive
shield	ceiling
siege	conceit
piece	receive

Two sorts of exceptions

- Words where the sound is not 'ee'
  ie and *ei* do not always make the sound 'ee'. If they make a different sound, then *ei* can be correct, even if there is no *c*.

  A lorry or a train can carry <u>freight</u> – pronounced 'frate'.

  If you check how tall you are, you measure your <u>height</u> – pronounced 'hite'.

  You control a horse with a <u>rein</u> – pronounced 'rane'.

- Words that break the rule
  There are fewer exceptions to this rule than most, but they do exist. These are some of the most common:

  weird   seize   protein

Need more practice? The examples on **page 14** should make things clear. If not, go back to the basic rule and make sure that you know exactly what it says.

The rule that isn't

There is *no* rule that says:

E before *i* if the sound isn't 'ee'.

In a word like *science*, the *i* and the *e* make separate sounds.

Fried is not pronounced 'freed'.

In *view* the pronunciation is 'vyoo', not 'vee'.

This does not stop *i* coming before *e* in all these cases.

Who says 'eyether'?

A tricky problem comes with words that can be said in different ways; in particular, *either* and *neither*.

There is even a song where two people disagree whether it should be 'eether' or 'eyether'.

There is no point in arguing which is correct; the fact is that both pronunciations are used.

But, for spelling purposes, take the 'eyether'/'neyether' pronunciation. The part of the rule that states: *when the sound is 'ee'* does not apply and the correct spellings are:

either   neither

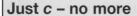

Just *c* – no more

What about words where *c* is followed by another consonant, then *ie/ei*?

The normal '*i* before *e*' rule applies.

In many cases (*client*, *cried*), the sound is not 'ee'.

But note such cases as *chief* and – a very difficult spelling in several ways – *mischievous*.

Helpful hints

Are there any other rules for the order of two vowels together? Not really, but here are two hints:

Ua/au – If the *u* is silent, it usually comes first: *guard*, *guarantee*. *Au* usually makes the sound 'or' or even 'o': *gauze*, *cause*, *haunt*, *cauliflower* – but note *gauge* (with silent *u*).

Ea/ae – *Ea* is the most commonly used (often, not always, sounded 'ee'): *peace*, *cheap*, *deal*, *head*, *heart*. You will find *ae* in some words from Latin like *Caesar* – and some Welsh place names.

Try it yourself!

What rule?

Turn to the activity on **page 16**.

All the words in this activity are correctly spelled. Your job is to decide which rule they follow, and then write them in your exercise book, using the rules given below as column headings.

I before e (no c/sound is 'ee')   E before i (c/sound is 'ee')

Sound not 'ee'/no rule applies   Exceptions to the rule

Check the answers on **pages 31–32**.

All correct?

Then move on . . .

Quick test

Copy the following sentences into your exercise book and, without looking back at any earlier rules or examples, underline the right version of the *ie/ei* words.

In the great hall, a shield/sheild on the cieling/ceiling contained the family coat of arms.

The cliffs rose to a great height/hieght, but the cheif/chief attraction was the view/veiw of the town below.

The priest/preist came to our meeting to receive/recieve the money we had raised.

The defenders yeilded/yielded after a long seige/siege when the enemy seized/siezed the opportunity for an assault.

Check your answers on **pages 31–32**.

Activities

Pages 15–18 contain activities based on different sections in the book. You will need to cut up these four pages, so remove them and photocopy them or copy them onto a blank sheet of paper, so that you can do the activities on both sides.

Using a dictionary (page 4)

A dictionary is arranged in alphabetical order: to begin with, by the first letters of words, then, if needed, in order of the second letter, third, fourth and so on.

Some people find it difficult to find their way through a dictionary, but it is very important for your spelling to be able to do so.

Cut out the 20 words below, spread them out on a table or desk and move them around until you have perfect alphabetical order. Then copy them into your exercise book.

scratch	smoke	best	scream
though	through	think	tribe
brother	brick	cream	crystal
screech	method	scrape	moth
beat	beast	cape	time

Activities

What rule? (page 14)

All the words below are correctly spelled. This activity is to help you understand the '*i* before *e*' rule.

Cut out the words, then place them in four columns or piles as follows:

- Words which have *i* before *e* because the sound is 'ee' and there is no c.
- Words which have *e* before *i* because the sound is 'ee' and they follow *c*.
- Words where *ie* or *ei* do not make the sound 'ee', so there is no rule.
- Words which are an exception to the rule.

quiet	caffeine	conceit	height
seize	siege	brief	tried
relief	deceive	either	friend
frieze	receipt	pier	ceiling

Now copy each pile of words into the right list in your exercise book, using the column headings given on **page 14**.

Activities

Games with affixes (page 22)

Below are three columns of words. The one on the left consists of **prefixes**, the one on the right of **suffixes**, and the one in the middle of the **main stems** of words. Not all the prefixes and suffixes are ones that we dealt with on **pages 21–22**.

Cut them all out, then see how many words you can form by mixing up different combinations. Join together two or three elements and use a prefix and suffix in the same word where you can. Use each affix or word stem as often as you like.

You might want to note them down to see how many you managed, or have a competition with your friends.

In your exercise book, write down all the words where you had to make a **change in the spelling**. An example is given at the bottom of the page.

un	**junction**	**ic**
dis	**glory**	**ion**
con	**like**	**er**
anti	**resolute**	**ly**
in	**noble**	**ous**
bio	**graph**	**al**
ir	**position**	**or**
co	**septic**	**able**
ig	**operate**	**tion**
pre	**describe**	**y**

Example: You could combine *ig*, *noble* and *ly* to form *ig-noble-ly* which shortens to *ignobly* and so belongs on your list of altered spellings. On the other hand, *ir-resolute-ly* spells *irresolutely*; there is no change and this does not belong on your list.

Activities

Find the definition (page 26)

In the left-hand column you will find a series of words. In each case, there are at least two words with the same sound, but different spellings.

In the right-hand column are brief definitions of those words.

Cut both lists out and put each word alongside the right definition.

When you are sure that the list is correct, copy it into your exercise book, as described on **page 26**.

wait	water plant/used in musical instruments
weight	a colour popular in football shirts
main	stay in one place/delay
mane	tranquillity/absence of war
programme	a part of a larger whole
program	heaviness
principal	belonging to them
principle	look at and study printed text
their	opposite of 'here'
there	hair of horse or lion
they're	organise or organiser/senior officer
compliment	chief/pipe for water or gas
complement	short for 'they are'
martial	item on television/sheet with details of concert
marshal	chief, as in head of school or college
reed	polite expression of praise
read	thing completing something else, e.g. a sentence
red	software instructions for computer
peace	warlike
piece	truth/ruling idea for conduct

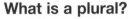

How to form plurals

Get started

What is a plural?

If you are writing or speaking about one person or thing, you use the **singular** form. If you want to refer to more than one, you need the **plural**. Can you work out the normal way to form the plural?

We saw a horse in that field.

My father bought a new car.

The horses lined up for the race.

There are too many cars in London.

In most cases, simply add *-s* (without an apostrophe) to form the plural.

Practice

Look out for exceptions . . .

- Add an *e*
  Try saying 'quizs' or 'sandwichs'. It is tricky.
  How would you say 'buss'? Exactly the same as the singular 'bus'.
  So add an *e* if the singular ends in *s, z, x, sh, ch* or any other sibilant sound: *quizzes, sandwiches, buses* and so on.

- Turn *y* into *ies*
  If the singular ends in a consonant followed by *y*, form the plural with *ies*:

  fly/flies   **lorry/lorries**   **enemy/enemies**

  Look at the note **Ending in *y*** on the right.

- No change
  Some words are exactly the same in singular and plural. You will need to learn what they are. The only clue is that they are mostly very common words, often referring to animals:

  sheep   **fish**   **deer**   **trout**

- Vowel change
  Sometimes, the ending of the word remains unchanged in the plural, but the vowel in the middle changes. This happens frequently with animals, people and parts of the body:

  goose/geese   **man/men**   **tooth/teeth**   **foot/feet**
  mouse/mice

Now check the note **Common differences** on the right.

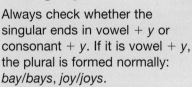

Ending in *y*

Always check whether the singular ends in vowel + *y* or consonant + *y*. If it is vowel + *y*, the plural is formed normally: *bay/bays, joy/joys*.

Remember the difference between *story* and *storey*:
- The first means a tale or a narrative and the plural is *stories*.
- The second means a floor in a building and the plural is *storeys*:

The adventure <u>stories</u> are kept in the upper <u>storeys</u> of the library.

Common differences

Irregular plurals usually apply to really basic things like animals we need for food, people we have to deal with or parts of our bodies:
- The *fish* we eat form an example of an unchanged plural, though we might refer to *fishes* swimming around.
- The *women* we meet and the *teeth* we eat with are examples of vowel change.
- The *children* we play with are a reminder of the old *-en* plural ending. Can you think of any more? Look on the next page for more examples.

Other unusual plurals

There are some plurals for which there is no rule:

- Do we turn *-f* into *-ves*?
  Sometimes: *knife/knives, loaf/loaves, half/halves*
  Sometimes not: *chief/chiefs, gulf/gulfs*.
  Sometimes there is a choice: *scarf/scarfs/scarves*
- Do we add *-e* after *o* at the end of the word?
  Sometimes: *potato/potatoes*
  Sometimes not: *piano/pianos*

Look for other examples in the **Try it yourself!** questions.

Plurals in *-en*

Adding *-en* used to be a common way of forming the plural, but there are very few words in common usage that use this rule today. Maybe you thought of *oxen* and, just possibly, *brethren*, an old form of *brothers*. Again, animals and people seem to have kept these ancient plurals.

Try it yourself!

Forming the plural

Copy the table below into your exercise book and fill in all the spaces:

Singular	Plural	Rule
train	trains	normal *s* plural
cherry		*y* into *ies*
	storeys	
life		
solo		
church		
proof		
	tomatoes	
	mice	change of vowel
tooth		
salmon		
country		
match		
	fines	
fox		

The correct answers are on **pages 31–32**.

Many words come into English from foreign languages – does this affect their plural form? Which of the following are correct?

The new **stadiums** have not been built.

The new **stadia** have not been built.

The garden centre sells **cactuses**.

The garden centre sells **cacti**.

Which did you choose? Both versions are correct. In most cases, it is possible to form the plural by adding an *-s* or *-es* to such words, just as if they were ordinary English words.

Spelling prefixes and suffixes

Get started

The general term for **prefixes** and **suffixes** is 'affixes'.

- A **prefix** is added to the *front* of a word with a set meaning and spelling, e.g. *semi-* (half), *anti-* (against), *un-* (not).
- A **suffix** is added to the *end* of a word with a set spelling and purpose, very often changing the part of speech (see *Practise Grammar*), e.g. *-ly* regularly forms an adverb, *-ous* regularly forms an adjective, *-ness* regularly forms a noun.
- Generally the spelling of affixes does not change. This section looks at exceptions.

Practice

In- and *con-*

These are two very common prefixes:

- *In-* means 'not' (it can also mean 'in').
- *Con-* means 'with' or 'together'.

They share one unusual feature: they change their spelling into forms that are easier to say:

- We say *invisible* (unable to be seen), but *impossible*, *irregular*, *ignoble* and *illegal*.
- *Con-* often appears as *com-* and sometimes as *co-*, *col-* or *cor-*. You *confide* in your *companion*. You might *cooperate* with him or her and *correspond* in a *colloquial* way.

Still unsure?

The basic point is very simple: sometimes *in-* and *com-* have a different spelling (and are said differently). Learn some common examples. (See **Try it yourself!** on **page 22**.)

Suffixes following *-y*

You learned in **How to form plurals** on **page 19** that, when a word ends with a consonant + *y*, the plural is formed by replacing the *y* with *ie* before adding *s*.

It is very similar with all suffixes: *y* turns into *i*.

friendly – friend**liness**   fury – fur**ious**   angry – ang**rily**

Again, if you need more practice, the examples in **Try it yourself!** should help.

Dis- or *diss-*?

Try to remember the set spellings of most affixes – especially words which cause spelling trouble such as *disappoint* and *disappear*.

The answer is simple. Remember that both words are built of a prefix (*dis-*, meaning 'not') and a word which contains a double *p*: *appoint* and *appear*.

Just remember how the word is built up and spelling problems disappear(!).

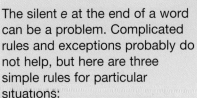

Disappearing *e*

The silent *e* at the end of a word can be a problem. Complicated rules and exceptions probably do not help, but here are three simple rules for particular situations:

- When the suffix is just *-y*, drop the *e* at the end of the word:
  stone/stony   wave/wavy
  spike/spiky   noise/noisy
  (Note: *y* in this example is used as a vowel, not a consonant.)
- Much the same happens when you add *-ly* to words ending in *e*. This time *-le* disappears:
  noble/nobly   gentle/gently
  subtle/subtly
- Often a word ends with an *e* to make its main vowel long (see page 3). When you add a suffix beginning with a consonant, keep the silent *e*:
  waste/wasteful
  shape/shapeless
  late/lateness

L, m, r or g?

Did you find a rule for which form of the prefixes in- or co- to use?

Probably not, but you should have been able to work out the sort of things that happen:

- R, l and m are used when the root word begins with that letter:
  irresistible/correct
  illegible/collect
  immature/commemorate
- M is also much used in front of p:
  impossible/comprehensive
- G is an oddity, sometimes used in front of n:
  ignore
  There are even one or two cog- words like this, e.g. cognitive.

-ible and -able

The most difficult of all suffixes is the one meaning 'able'. When is it -ible and when -able?

Sadly, any rules that exist are more complicated than just learning the spellings, but here is one little hint:

If the main part of the word is an ordinary English word, the ending is almost certainly -able. For example:

uneatable – inedible
believable – credible

Try it yourself!

What form of the prefix?

One letter has been left out in each of the following words. In those on the left it is the second letter, following i. In those on the right it is the third letter, following co.

The normal forms of these prefixes are in- and con-, but that is not always the right answer. It is up to you to insert the right letter as you copy the words into your exercise book. Remember that co- might be the right answer, in which case you add nothing.

i__sincere	co__tact
i__secure	co__memorate
i__norant	co__ference
i__legible	co__rect
i__resistible	co__lect
i__possible	co__ordinate
i__mature	co__prehensive
i__edible	co__fer

Check the answers on **pages 31–32**.

All correct?

Now, can you work out a rule for which form of the prefix to use?

Check your idea in the note L, m, r or g? on the left.

Games with affixes

Turn to **page 17** and follow the instructions for this activity.

You are asked to join up affixes and the main root of words to create longer words, then to write in your exercise book any words you make that involve a slight change of spelling.

Check your answers on **pages 31–32**. The last part of the activity is the only part for which answers are given.

Same sound, different spelling: 1

Often, in English, two or more words which are spelled differently sound the same. This section and the next deal with some common and important cases. It is not possible for it to be a complete list, though.

Get started

Sometimes you just have to learn the right spelling by heart. Sometimes, though, it can help to work out where the word comes from or what other words it is connected with:

- Take the word *no* (rhymes with *blow*) which you can link to other negatives like *nowhere* and *nothing*.
- If you add *w*, it turns into *now* which rhymes with *cow*, not with *blow*.
- Put a silent *k* on the front and the word *know* sounds like *no* and means 'to be aware of'.

These just have to be learned, but, when it comes to a word like *knowledge*, you can work out the correct spelling. It may rhyme with *college*, but you can see that it belongs with *know*.

Practice

To, two, too

Probably the simplest set of words that sound the same are *to*, *too* and *two*.

Do you know when to use each one?

A useful tip is to learn the meanings of *too* and *two* and use *to* for all other cases:

- *Two* is a number (2).
- *Too* has two uses. It can mean 'also': **My brother came, too.** It can also mean 'more than you expect or want or can deal with': **The English homework was too difficult.**

There, their, they're

Work out the spellings from their meanings:

- *There* is linked with *here*. They are opposites in meaning ('here and there') and are spelled the same with one letter added. You also use *there* in sentences like: **There are two weeks left.**
- *Their* (meaning 'belonging to them') is linked with *they*. Often, a letter *y* turns into *i*, so that reminds you that the spelling is *the(y)ir*, not *ie*.
- *They're* is short for *they are*, with an apostrophe for a missing letter.

Still unsure? Look at **A reminder** on the right.

The past is a problem

Forming the past tense often involves adding *-ed*. Sometimes the sound is 't' and the spelling fits in with this:

I <u>meant</u> to get my homework finished.

But, in the past tense of the verb *to pass*, we say 'past', but we must spell it *passed*. Look at the difference between *past* and *passed*:

In the <u>past</u> I <u>passed</u> all my tests.
We went <u>past</u> the cinema.
or
We <u>passed</u> the cinema.

Make the connection

Where possible, link meanings of words together to help you remember the spelling. There may seem to be no sense in spelling the number as *two* when there is no *w* sound. But, if you think of *twin*, you can connect to a word where the *w* is still sounded.

A reminder

The '*i* before *e*' rule does not apply to *their* – the sound is not 'ee'.

They're means 'they are' and nothing else.

If in doubt, use *there* as the most common spelling.

Definitions

- Its/it's: *Its* means 'belonging to it'. *It's* is short for 'it is' or 'it has'.
- Way/weigh/weight/wait: *Way* means 'route', 'direction' or 'method'. *Weigh* means 'measure how heavy' (as in *weight*). *Wait* means 'pause' or 'delay'.
- Roll/role: *Roll* can mean many things, e.g. a breadcake, a list, to turn over and over. A *role* is a part in a play.
- Draft/draught: A *draft* is a first or early version of something. The most common meaning of *draught* is 'a current of air'.
- Plain/plane: *Plain* means 'simple' or 'obvious' and is also open land. *Plane* is short for 'aeroplane' and also a tool in woodwork.
- Sew/sow: *Sew* is to stitch with a needle and thread. *Sow* means 'to plant seeds'.

Try it yourself!

Choose the right spelling

Below are four sentences with either *there*, *their* or *they're* or *to*, *too* or *two* left out. Copy the sentences into your exercise book and write in the correct words.

> Sarah, Louise and _____ cousins decided _____ go _____ after school.
>
> _____ far _____ late _____ put _____ names down for the trip.
>
> I was _____ late, _____.
>
> By the time I spoke _____ Mrs Chowdhury, _____ were only _____ days _____ go.

Check your answers on **pages 31–32**.

All correct?

If not, remind yourself that the most used spellings are *to* and *there*. Then turn back to **page 23** and re-learn the definitions of *two*, *too*, *their* and *they're*.

Which one is right?

Here are some examples of words which sound the same, but are spelled differently. Choose the best word from the list to fill each gap in the sentences and then write the completed sentences in your exercise book:

role/roll	plain/plane	draft/draught	sew/sow
its/it's	weight/wait	weigh/way	

> Which is the best _____ to the cinema?
>
> _____ nearly time to catch the bus.
>
> I'm hoping to get the lead _____ in the school play.
>
> According to the school _____ there are 500 pupils.
>
> The first _____ of my story had a lot of mistakes.
>
> The truth was _____ for all to see.
>
> Now is the right time to _____ your seeds.
>
> The dog was wagging _____ tail.
>
> Slimmers have to _____ themselves regularly.
>
> The _____ was a Boeing 757.
>
> I felt the _____ from the open window.
>
> Having to _____ so long became boring.

Check your answers on **pages 31–32**. **All correct?**

If not, read the note **Definitions** on the left carefully and work out why your answers were wrong.

Same sound, different spelling: 2

Get started

We looked at the difference between *sow* and *sew* in the last section.

Both are pronounced the same, but the first is planting, the second is stitching. There is also the word *so*, as in: **Spelling is _so_ confusing.**

But you can also take the word *sow*, say it differently, and you have a female pig. So sometimes the spelling is the same but the sound is different.

Practice

But are there others?

Of course:

- What does *tear* say? You say 'teer' when it means 'water in the eye', and 'tare' when it means 'rip'. And, of course, there is a word *tare*, not very common, but meaning a plant or weed and also a term for the weight of lorries.

- *Lead* can be pronounced two ways, with a short *e* for the metal, with a long *e* as a verb meaning 'to take or direct'. And, once again, there is another spelling, *led*, which sounds like the metal, but is the past tense of the verb.

- Another confusing *ea* word is *read*. If it sounds the same as *reed* (a water plant), it is the present tense of the verb for studying print. The past tense is spelled the same, *read*, but it sounds the same as *red*, the colour. If you live in Berkshire, you may even be *reading* ('reeding') this in *Reading* ('Redding').

The rule is to *learn the simple words*. See the note on the right.

American spellings and computers

There are many different American spellings, like *color* instead of *colour*, which can be confusing.

It is not wrong to use these, but in this country it is a little odd.

But what about *program* and *disk*? These are the American spellings of *programme* and *disc*.

Because the language of computers has grown up in the USA, even in Britain these are the correct spellings for a computer disk or program.

But we do keep the British spelling for *a concert programme*, *a television programme* or *a programme of events*.

And the sun remains a *disc* and an injured back can be a *slipped disc*.

More about *its*

Definitions (page 24), briefly dealt with *its* and *it's*.

One of the most common errors in spelling is putting an apostrophe in *its* when it means 'belonging to it'. We do not put an apostrophe in *his* or *hers*, so why *its*?

The apostrophe in *it's* shows where *i* or *ha* has been left out:

It has fallen behind the chair.
It's fallen behind the chair.

It is too late to start now.
It's too late to start now.

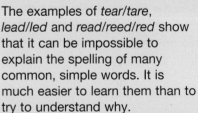

Learn the simple words

The examples of *tear/tare*, *lead/led* and *read/reed/red* show that it can be impossible to explain the spelling of many common, simple words. It is much easier to learn them than to try to understand why.

Remember: new spellings should be written in your word book.

If the difficulty is which-spelling-with-which-meaning, write a short definition:

lead – metal or present tense of verb

led – past tense of verb

Fun for puns

Can you make a list for yourself of other words that sound the same, but have different spellings? There are many you could find.

There are also, of course, plenty of words that have the same sound and spelling, but quite different meanings.

You can have fun with jokes that use the different meanings of words or different words that sound the same.

These jokes are called puns. See if you get the joke . . .

His death, which happened in his berth,

At forty-odd befell.

They went and told the sexton

And the sexton tolled the bell.

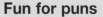

Try it yourself!

Find the definition

Turn to the activity on **page 18**.

You will find a number of words listed. In each case, there are at least two words which sound the same, but have different spellings.

Your task is to match each word with the correct definition.

Some of the words will be familiar from **pages 23–25**, and some will be new to you. See how many you know.

Create a table in your exercise book like the one started below and fill out the rest of the answers. The first has been done for you.

Word	Definition
wait	**stay in one place/delay**

Check your answers on **pages 31–32**.

All correct?

You might have made a mistake on some of the new words.

Do not worry. Just make sure that you learn them now: the difference between *peace* and *piece*, perhaps, or between *principal* and *principle*.

Do not forget to use your word book.

Difficult spellings

Get started

A difficult spelling is any spelling that you find hard to get right. You might be able to spell all sorts of long words correctly, but have a blind spot on some apparently simple five-letter word. So you must take charge of your own spelling:

- If your problem words are not in this book, they will certainly be in the dictionary.
- When spelling, your best friends are your own word book, your memory – and, of course, your teacher.

These last two sections deal with the sorts of words you are likely to have difficulty with: long words in common use, words you can confuse with each other, words with problems over single and double letters, etc.

Practice

There is a group of fairly common words that begin with *th* and use *ou*, *gh* or both, all with slightly different pronunciations. Take a look at these:

though	**Though** the work was hard, we finished in time.
through	**My father had to drive <u>through</u> the snow.**
thought	**I <u>thought</u> I knew the answer.**
thorough	**This is a very <u>thorough</u> account.**
throughout	**He was reading a comic <u>throughout</u> the lesson.**

Remember:

- There is only one *gh* in each word.
- All vowels are *ou* except at the beginning of *thorough*.
- Use *r* or *t* (on its own, not in *th*) where you hear the sound of *r* or *t*.

But you still need to separate these words from *threw*:

I <u>threw</u> the ball <u>through</u> the window.

and *throat*:

The doctor gave my <u>throat</u> a <u>thorough</u> examination.

Spelling's Top Ten

In 1999, a survey found that these were the ten most commonly misspelled words:

accommodate	disastrous
humorous	millennium
mischievous	pronunciation
privilege	separate
weird	surprise

Only eight per cent of 16–24-year-olds could spell them all correctly!

Some have been dealt with already in this book. Some of the others are referred to in this or the next section. You should make sure that you can spell them all correctly.

Be careful

A regular problem is with *-ful* endings.

Because the suffix *-ful* means the same as *full*, it is tempting to spell it the same way.

But one *l* is enough:

hopeful	cheerful	beautiful
helpful	awful	

Note also *fulfil*.

The *l* is only doubled when a vowel sound (in this case *y* is a vowel) is added:

hopefully fulfilling

Changes in the middle

Sometimes, when words of more than one syllable gain an extra suffix, a change hits the middle vowel. Here are some words that need great care:

- Maintenance – This comes from the word *maintain* and some people actually say 'maintainance', so perhaps it is not surprising that the spelling goes the same way. Learn to say it properly and the rest is easy: stress the first syllable, say the second as 'ten'.

- Words ending in *-our* – Depending on the ending, the *u* can disappear. This is particularly true with the *-ous* ending:
  vigour/vigorous
  humour/humorous
  dolour/dolorous
  Do not do this with words like *colourful* or *colouring* (although there are one or two obscure words from *colour* where it does happen).

- Verbs ending in *-ounce* – This time it is *o* that disappears when you form a noun with *-ation*. The silent *e* also changes, but that is normal:
  denounce/denunciation
  renounce/renunciation
  The most used of these is *pronounce/pronunciation*. Like *maintenance*, the pronunciation of *pronunciation* matters. People who say 'pronounciation' tend to spell it wrong.

Try it yourself!

The *th*s

In the following short piece of writing, every word that begins with *th* has been left incomplete. Copy the passage into your exercise book, completing the word each time. Some are easy (you should have no trouble with *the*!), others relate to difficulties considered on **pages 23 and 27**.

> Faced with a decision, Mr Wilson th_____ deeply for a while, giving th_____ matter th_____ consideration. Th_____ th_____ th_____ years he had been Head of th_____ school, he had encouraged pupils to bring th_____ complaints to him th_____ th_____ school council. Th_____ th_____ had been one or two disagreements, th_____ council had mostly given any difficulties much th_____ and expressed th_____ views sensibly. Now th_____ had suggested th_____ in future pupils should write reports on teachers, instead of th_____ other way round. Mr Wilson finally decided th_____ th_____ was out of th_____ question. 'Th_____ definitely going too far th_____ time,' he muttered, 'th_____ some of th_____ results might be interesting.'

Check your answers on **pages 31–32**.

All correct?

If not:
- Check **page 23** for *there*, *their*, *they're*.
- Check **page 27** for *though*, *through*, *thought*, *thorough*, *throughout*.
- Or just work out what you did wrong – any other mistakes are probably just simple misunderstandings.

A few last difficulties

Get started

A frequent difficulty comes in the form of what are called **agent nouns**. These are the nouns that apply to the person (sometimes the thing) doing an act:

football/football<u>er</u>   employ/employ<u>er</u>   ride/rid<u>er</u>

All the examples above use *-er* which is the most common ending. But, for no obvious reason, there are plenty of exceptions:

profess<u>or</u>	schol<u>ar</u>
doct<u>or</u>	burgl<u>ar</u>
visit<u>or</u>	vic<u>ar</u>
jur<u>or</u>	pedl<u>ar</u>
propriet<u>or</u>	burs<u>ar</u>
accelerat<u>or</u>	

Still unsure?

The simple rules are:

- If in doubt, use *-er*. This fits the majority of cases – and, almost certainly, any new words that have to be invented.
- Learn the *-or* and *-ar* words you are likely to need.
- For the opposite meaning, *-ee* is a useful ending.

  An employ<u>er</u> employs an employ<u>ee</u>.

Practice

Many words begin with *exe-* and many others begin with *exce-*. How do you tell the difference?

If you speak and listen carefully, the extra *c* sound might tell you. Otherwise it is a matter of learning which is which:

exceed	excellent	execute	exercise
except	excess	exert	exemplary

Difficulties can be sorted out by using a dictionary. The problem comes at the start of a word, so finding the right spelling is easy.

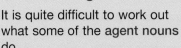

A note on agent nouns

It is quite difficult to work out what some of the agent nouns do.

Obviously a *rider* rides and a *burglar* burgles, but what does a *professor* profess and what does a *bursar* or a *doctor* do?

Do not worry. These are agent nouns like the others. What they are doing goes back to the ancient origins of the word. For instance, *bursa* is the Latin word for 'purse', so a *bursar* in a school or college is like a *purser* on a ship: he or she looks after the money!

And then there's *acc*

Words beginning with *exce-* can also be confused with words beginning with *acc-*.

If *acc-* is followed by a consonant or *a, o* or *u*, both the *c* sounds are hard, so we just have one sound (*account*). If *acc-* is followed by *e* or *i*, we make two *c* sounds: hard, then soft.

Just memorise (and, perhaps, write in your word book) these two common examples:

accept	receive or agree
except	apart from, with the exception of
access	way in/obtain data
excess	too much of something

I <u>accept</u> that I could try harder in all my subjects <u>except</u> English.

With the new program I had <u>access</u> to an <u>excess</u> of information I didn't need.

English or French?

When working out the meaning and spelling of words it can sometimes help to know which foreign language they come from.

On the other hand, it is sometimes confusing when a word has a similar, but different, spelling in, for instance, French. Double letters can be a problem:

In France, you would find a person's *adresse* to go to his *appartement*.

In England, you would find his *address* to go to his *apartment*.

It is simply a matter of learning both:
- Write one spelling in your French vocabulary book.
- Write the other in your English word book.

Try it yourself!

The last test

For this last test, you may be asked about anything from anywhere in the book.

You have a series of clues, some of them a bit like crossword clues.

Write your answers to the clues in your exercise book. Each answer must be correctly spelled and there is one key letter in every answer that you should underline (e.g. underline the 3rd letter in the first clue).

If you read all these letters as a series of words, they will make up a message.

If your answers do not spell out a message, at least one is wrong, so try again!

The first has been done for you.

Which word has a short o: coast or cost?	(3rd letter)	cos<u>t</u>
An exception to the '*i* before *e*' rule/important in diet	(1st letter)	
Belonging to them	(3rd letter)	
A silent *t* in a sharp emblem of Scotland	(6th letter)	
Very good indeed, but not exemplary	(6th letter)	
Add a prefix to *legible* to mean 'can't be read'	(1st letter)	
An upright pillar (like Nelson's) with a silent letter	(6th letter)	
A dwarf, a popular garden ornament – silent letter, again	(1st letter)	
A hard g which should be soft/a light laugh	(2nd letter)	
A passage in a church, aeroplane or supermarket	(3rd letter)	
A silent h in a plant we eat stewed	(6th letter)	
Your _____ tells how tall you are	(2nd letter)	
I should have or *I should of*? (One-word answer)	(2nd letter)	
A nine-letter word meaning *chief* starts with *p*	(9th letter)	
Celebrated in 2000 with dome, bridge, stadium, etc.	(4th letter)	
The plural of *storey* (floor of a building)	(6th letter)	
Learning, begins with a silent *k* and rhymes with *college*	(6th letter)	
Eight-letter word begins with *s* and is the opposite of *together*	(4th letter)	
Study of the mind begins with silent p	(2nd letter)	
Form an adverb from *happy: We played _____*.	(7th letter)	

Check your answers on **pages 31–32**.

Did you form the message?

Do you agree with it?!

Answers

THE LONG AND SHORT OF IT (PAGE 4)

Short	Long	What makes the vowel long?
best	beast	extra vowel added
fin	fine	e added at the end
cot	coat	extra vowel added
hit	height	extra vowel and silent *gh* added
red	reed	e doubled
hop	hope	e added at the end
bran	brain	extra vowel added
tun	tune	e added at the end

USING A DICTIONARY (PAGE 4)

beast, beat, best, brick, brother, cape, cream, crystal, method, moth, scrape, scratch, scream, screech, smoke, think, though, through, time, tribe

JOINING VOWELS TOGETHER (PAGE 6)

nuisance, fault, dear, persuade, aunt, because, teeth/tooth, really, pained, coat, train, spoiled, wailed, too, keen, joining, said

HOW HARD IS THIS? (PAGE 8)

cell, cricket, gigantic, gymnasium (or gym), gorgeous, coffee, force, courageous, singing, geography, centre

FILL THE GAPS (PAGE 8)

photography, matches, conscientious, psychology, mathematics, shoe-shine, theatre, mashed, church

FILL IN THE SILENT LETTER (PAGE 10)

wreck, wrinkle, thought, knowledge, ghost, scissors, gnash, knit, castle, rhythm, calm, throughout, debt, yacht, knuckle, receipt, mistletoe, thumb, wrist, pneumatic

SPELLING FOR MEANING (PAGE 10)

knight, scent, knew, right, know, wrap, wring, knot, rite

ACCORDING TO THE RULE (PAGE 12)

fatten, faded, running, crossed, tripped, collect, baker, blaming, crammed, flaking, battered, cutting, scissors, crater, napping

A MIXED BAG (PAGE 12)

hopeful, getting, prison, innocent, banned, protest, steered, trouble, never, committed, criminal, before, arrest

WHAT RULE? (PAGE 14)

I before e (no c/sound is 'ee')
brief, relief, frieze, pier, siege

E before i (c/sound is 'ee')
conceit, deceive, receipt, ceiling

Sound not 'ee'/no rule applies
quiet, either, height, tried, friend

Exceptions to the rule
seize, caffeine

QUICK TEST (PAGE 14)

shield, ceiling; height, chief, view; priest, receive; yielded, siege, seized

FORMING THE PLURAL (PAGE 20)

Singular	Plural	Rule
train	trains	normal s plural
cherry	cherries	y into ies
storey	storeys	normal s plural
life	lives	f into ves
solo	solos	normal s plural
church	churches	add es after sibilant
proof	proofs	normal s plural
tomato	tomatoes	add extra e after final o
mouse	mice	change of vowel
tooth	teeth	change of vowel
salmon	salmon	unchanged plural
country	countries	y into ies
match	matches	add es after sibilant
fine	fines	normal s plural
fox	foxes	add es after sibilant

WHAT FORM OF THE PREFIX? (PAGE 22)

insincere, insecure, ignorant, illegible, irresistible, impossible, immature, inedible, contact, commemorate, conference, correct, collect, coordinate, comprehensive, confer

Answers

GAMES WITH AFFIXES (PAGE 22)

Words with changed spelling only

ignobly, resolution, glorious, inglorious, inoperable, nobly, operable, operation, operator, indescribable, describable, description, describer (*Likable* and *likeable* are both correct.)

Some of these are very difficult. If you found 7 out of 14, that is pretty good. Probably there are several more which we missed.

CHOOSE THE RIGHT SPELLING (PAGE 24)

Sarah, Louise and their cousins decided to go there after school.

They're far too late to put their names down for the trip.

I was too late, too.

By the time I spoke to Mrs Chowdhury, there were only two days to go.

WHICH ONE IS RIGHT? (PAGE 24)

way, it's, role, roll, draft, plain, sow, its, weigh, plane, draught, wait

FIND THE DEFINITION (PAGE 26)

Word	Definition
wait	stay in one place/delay
weight	heaviness
main	chief/pipe for water or gas
mane	hair of horse or lion
programme	item on television/sheet with details of concert
program	software instructions for computer
principal	chief, as in head of school or college
principle	truth/ruling idea for conduct
their	belonging to them
there	opposite of 'here'
they're	short for 'they are'
compliment	polite expression of praise
complement	thing completing something else, e.g. a sentence
martial	warlike
marshal	organise or organiser/senior officer
reed	water plant/used in musical instruments
read	look at and study printed text
red	a colour popular in football shirts
peace	tranquillity/absence of war
piece	a part of a larger whole

THE *TH*S (PAGE 28)

Faced with a decision, Mr Wilson thought deeply for a while, giving the matter thorough consideration. Throughout the three/thirteen/thirty years he had been Head of the school, he had encouraged pupils to bring their complaints to him through the school council. Though there had been one or two disagreements, the council had mostly given any difficulties much thought and expressed their views sensibly. Now they had suggested that in future pupils should write reports on teachers, instead of the other way round. Mr Wilson finally decided that this was out of the question.
'They're definitely going too far this time,' he muttered, 'though some of the results might be interesting.'

THE LAST TEST (PAGE 30)

co<u>s</u>t, <u>p</u>rotein, th<u>ei</u>r, thist<u>l</u>e, excel<u>l</u>ent, <u>i</u>llegible, colum<u>n</u>, <u>g</u>nome, <u>g</u>iggle, a<u>i</u>sle, rhuba<u>r</u>b, h<u>ei</u>ght, h<u>a</u>ve, principa<u>l</u>, mil<u>l</u>ennium, store<u>y</u>s, knowl<u>ed</u>ge, sepa<u>r</u>ate, <u>p</u>sychology, happil<u>y</u>

Final message: SPELLING IS REALLY EASY (if you go about it the right way!)